REAL-LIFE MATHS

Ten ways to teach key maths concepts in rich and relevant scenarios

AGES 5 TO 7

IIII SPRINGBOKS
IIII IIII III ZEBRAS
I GIRAFFES

GIRAFFE

WEIGHT 1200 kg

HEIGHT = 530 cm

WEIGHT = 45 kg

SPRINGBOK

WEIGHT = 320 kg

HEIGHT = 70 cm

HEIGHT = 130cm

ZEBRA

Includes FREE CD-ROM

SCHOLASTIC

Book End, Range Road, Witney, Oxfordshire, OX29 OYD
www.scholastic.co.uk
© 2013, Scholastic Ltd
3 4 5 6 7 8 9   5 6 7 8 9 1 2

British Library Cataloguing-in-Publication Data
A catalogue record for this book is available from the
British Library.

ISBN 978-1407-12791-0
Printed by Bell & Bain Ltd, Glasgow

Text © Paul Hollin 2013

Commissioning Editor
Paul Naish

Development Editor
Emily Jefferson

Editor
Mary Nathan

Proofreader
Kate Pedlar

Series Designer
Shelley Best

Illustrator
Paul Hutchison

Acknowledgements
The publishers gratefully acknowledge permission
to reproduce the following copyright material:

Cover: safari © Peter ten Broecke/iStockphoto.com
Page 41: pop_jop/iStockphoto.com

About the author
Paul Hollin worked for many years in teaching,
starting as a maths tutor for the Home Tutors
Teachers' Cooperative in London. After stints
doing photography in youth clubs and teaching
English in Spain and London, he eventually became
a primary teacher working mainly with junior-aged
children. He left the classroom to work for Sherston
Software, where he designed a wide range of
educational software and now works in
educational publishing, writing and providing
consultancy in a freelance capacity.

Contents

About the series

Real-Life Maths is a series of three books designed to supplement your maths curriculum. Each book provides a wide range of extended scenarios that develop many maths skills in engaging and meaningful contexts, often involving significant child interaction. The three books are categorised by age range, although teachers will find materials suitable for their classes across the series as the activities are relatively age neutral. The planning grids for the books are available on each respective CD-ROM.

The importance of real-life maths

Anyone who keeps their eye on the educational news will know that maths is a hot topic: standards aren't good enough; adults can't add up; other countries do it better, and so on. Why is it thus? It is interesting to compare maths with literacy; between the two they form the bedrock of primary education. There are many technical aspects to developing a child's capabilities in literacy – these are sometimes taught discretely and sometimes integrated. Either way, every primary school in the land uses real sources of language, such as books, newspapers and drama, to aid pupils' literacy development; not to mention the myriad of approaches for writing in context – letters, stories, poems, and more.

Now look at maths. The majority of maths lessons involve the discrete teaching of specific skills, be it the four operations, factors, or shape. The nature of maths dictates this to some extent, but it can leave those being taught it fundamentally baffled – why are they learning it? Now, *we* know why – being numerate is essential in adult life – but, and here's the crux of the matter, in adult life nearly all of us use our numeracy skills in meaningful situations. These books do not suggest that you should fundamentally alter your maths curriculum, but by simply adding a regular dose of real-life maths, as well as engaging and motivating your pupils, they will see the point of it all. Real-life maths activities are not just about getting the right answers. Mistakes can be useful, allowing children to see that the consequence of an error is not simply a cross and a correction: an error might result in an incorrect design, getting lost, or even losing money.

About the activities

There are ten real-life scenarios per book, each one providing a multi-session, structured scenario complete with teacher guidance and resources on paper and the accompanying CD-ROM. Typically, a scenario will take between two and four lessons to complete. Every scenario has a practical focus, where the maths is an integral part of a greater task – just like life!

The scenarios are arranged in roughly increasing levels of difficulty, and between them they cover a wide range of maths skills, often with several skills being involved in any one activity. In addition, because of their focus on the real world, the scenarios have cross-curricular links, and most primary subjects are covered.

The activities are all fairly challenging. They require extended thinking and clear organisation of work, as well as making demands on children's mathematical thinking. Some can be done by individuals, though many would benefit from paired or group work, and some involve whole-class participation in highly 'immersive' situations.

Scenario content

Each scenario covers four pages in the book, and typically consists of:

1. Teacher notes

Mathematics coverage; guidance on organising and running lessons; tips for differentiation; review and further ideas.

2. Scenario guidelines

Introducing the scenario; guidelines and 'rules'; additional information; worked examples where appropriate.

3. Resources and information

Typically this page has all of the mathematical and factual information needed to run the scenario.

4. Recording sheet

Typically this page provides a template for children to use to lay out their work, though sometimes additional paper is required.

CD-ROM content

For every activity there is extensive supporting material on the CD-ROM, including an introductory video and slideshow, which set the scene. In addition, all photocopiables are available on the CD-ROM for easy printing. Most activities have further support sheets which can be printed, and some have additional resources, such as simple chart and graphing tools.

Planning and running real-life maths sessions

Good learning and good lessons come at a price – real-life maths scenarios require preparation. Teachers will need to familiarise themselves with the scenario in advance, as well as prepare resources.

How you weave the lessons into your curriculum will depend on your general approach to teaching. Do you want to challenge children by presenting activities that are in their 'zone of development', or do you prefer to consolidate well-honed skills?

Typically, the first lesson is about introducing the scenario to the class. There is an introduction for each activity on the CD-ROM which, while not essential, does provide a clear overview of the context and situation. In addition, introducing or recapping the key maths skills involved is encouraged. Children may also need to do some planning in advance of the second lesson.

The second lesson is where the scenario really gets underway. Ideally, having more than an hour available would be useful if things are progressing well. However long you spend, a plenary review is encouraged afterwards, where broader issues of the purpose of the maths as well as the maths skills involved can be discussed.

Subsequent lessons, either repetitions with variation or extensions, are also possible at your discretion – and if you are inspired there are ideas for further work in the teacher notes for each scenario, as well as guidance at the back of the book.

Remember, the activities in all three books are relatively age neutral, and can be used effectively to challenge or support children in other age groups, and all three books' planning grids are on the CD-ROM.

Ages 5–7	Pages 8–11	Pages 12–15	Pages 16–19	Pages 20–23	Pages 24–27
Scenario	1. Rat-a-tat Zoo	2. Red Riding Hood's postal service	3. Pirate birthdays	4. A big day out	5. Playground champs
Focus	Simple composition and rhythm activities to develop counting skills and number awareness.	Help Red Riding Hood sort out the stamps for her customers' letters.	Sorting birth dates by days, then months, and finally chronologically.	Plan a trip around Tinytown for Tina the Teddy using the map.	Children take part in a virtual sports day, with random results generation for different scores every time.
Difficulty rating (3 max.)	★	★	★	★★	★★
Maths covered	• Counting to 16 • Odd and even • Reading numbers	• Colours and shapes • Number bonds to 20 • Simple pictograms • Simple money optional • Length and weight (optional)	• Sorting by days and months • Ordering between 1 and 100 • Finding differences between dates (extension)	• Directions/turns • Simple coordinates • Distances (optional) • Adding time (optional)	• Understanding place value • Adding tens • Cardinal/ordinal numbers
Cross-curricular links	• Music: composing, rhythm and dynamics • ICT: simple charts	• Literacy: speaking and listening • ICT: data handling	• Literacy: speaking and listening • History: basic chronology	• Literacy: speaking and listening • Geography: simple maps and keys	• PE: sport awareness.
CD-ROM material	• Introductory slideshow • PDFs of photocopiables • Additional composing sheets • Images of percussion instruments	• Introductory slideshow • PDFs of photocopiables • Pictogram tool • Blank stamp charts • Harder stamp prices	• Introductory slideshow • Meet the crew • PDFs of photocopiables • Large game charts • Support and extension photocopiables	• Introductory slideshow • PDFs of photocopiables • Colour and blank maps • Additional game 'The Tinytown challenge'	• Introductory slideshow • Random results generator • PDFs of photocopiables • Excel spreadsheet
Resources needed	Photocopiables, pencils, percussion instruments or objects to bang	Photocopiables, coloured pens/pencils, scissors, glue sticks	Photocopiables, pencils, paper, glue sticks, calendar showing days (optional)	Photocopiables, pencils, counters and small teddy (optional)	Photocopiables, pencils and paper
Timescales	Minimum three sessions, around 30 minutes per session	Minimum two sessions, 30–60 minutes for main activity	Minimum two sessions, 1 hour maximum per session	Minimum two sessions, approximately 1 hour each	Minimum two sessions, 30–60 minutes each
Organisation	Individual, paired or small groups	Individual or paired; whole class or carousel activity	Groups of 2–4 children	Individual or paired	Individual or paired, plus cross checking work

Ages 5–7 continued	Pages 28–31	Pages 32–35	Pages 36–39	Pages 40–43	Pages 44–47
Scenario	6. Magical mosaics	7. Shopalot	8. Frieda's Fruit Farm	9. On safari	10. Gloria's Glorious Gardens
Focus	Design unique mosaics and calculate tiles and costs.	Take on the roles of stallholders and shoppers, buying and selling goods.	Work on or visit Frieda's Fruit Farm, buying and selling berries.	A virtual trip to the Etosha National Park in Namibia to research wildlife.	Design and cost a range of bespoke gardens to fit different customers' needs.
Difficulty rating (3 max.)	★★	★★	★★★	★★★	★★★
Maths covered	● Understanding shape, symmetry, counting ● Multiplication or counting in 2s, 5s, 10s to calculate costs	● Number bonds to 20 (to 100 optional) ● Money: £1 coins, £5 & £10 notes	● Times tables ● Adding and subtracting money ● Organising longer tasks	● Estimating ● Understanding units ● Using larger numbers ● Creating charts/diagrams	● Multiplying by 2,3,4,5 and by 10, 20,30 and 40 ● Adding HTU for costs ● Simple scale and measures
Cross-curricular links	● Art: creating designs	● Literacy: speaking and listening ● D&T: logo design, clothes design ● PSHE: financial awareness	● Literacy: speaking and listening ● PSHE: healthy eating, financial awareness	● Literacy: speaking and listening, reading, writing ● Science: living things ● ICT: data handling	● Literacy: speaking and listening ● D&T: design ● PSHE: financial awareness
CD-ROM material	● Introductory slideshow ● PDFs of photocopiables ● 1cm² planning grid ● Customer requests	● Introductory slideshow ● PDFs of photocopiables ● Goods for extra stalls ● Paper money ● Headbands and wallets	● Introductory slideshow ● PDFs of photocopiables ● Pictures of berries ● Paper money	● Introductory videos ● PDFs of photocopiables ● Chart, tally chart, Carroll diagram and pictogram tools ● Useful links and info	● Introductory slideshow ● PDFs of photocopiables ● Scale plans, pics of items ● 1cm² planning grid ● Gloria says yes/no
Resources needed	Photocopiables, pencils, squared paper, rulers; coloured pencils/pens; counters, interlocking cubes for support	Photocopiables, pencils, colours, paper, glue sticks, paper money and plastic pound coins (optional)	Photocopiables, pencils, paper, plastic or paper money; containers for carrying goods	Photocopiables, pencils, paper; books about African wildlife or internet access (optional)	Photocopiables, pencils, paper, rulers and calculators (optional)
Timescales	Minimum two sessions, 1 hour or more per session	Minimum two sessions, around 1 hour per session	Minimum two sessions, around 1 hour per session	Minimum three sessions, around 1 hour per session	Minimum two sessions, 1 hour or more per session
Organisation	Individual, paired or small groups	Whole-class, pupils in 'role', lots of movement	Individual or paired; whole-class or carousel	Individual, paired or groups	Individual, paired or small groups

Rat-a-tat Zoo

Overview
Children carry out simple composition and rhythm activities to develop counting skills and number awareness.

Timescales
- Lesson 1 (about 30 minutes): Introduce key concepts and the scenario.
- Lesson 2 (about 30 minutes): Run the session and children perform to the class.
- Repeating (about 30 minutes): Allow children to compose for different animals, using new instruments if possible.
- Extension: Challenge children to work in small groups and create multi-instrument compositions.

Maths covered
- Counting to at least 16.
- Odd and even numbers.
- Reading numbers.

Prior learning
Children should have some familiarity with counting to ten and beyond.

Cross-curricular links
- Music: composing, rhythm and dynamics.
- ICT: simple charts.

CD-ROM resources list
- Scenario video and slideshow.
- Photocopiables: *Scenario guidelines, Animal cards, Composition sheet, Additional composing bars, Typical percussion instruments.*

Resource list
Pencils, percussion instruments or suitable objects for tapping and banging.

Setting the scene
Watch the introduction on the CD-ROM, which highlights key musical terms and shows pictures of a range of animals. Discuss the nature of the compositions (they only use percussion). Draw out observations about the different pieces: the rhythm; loudness versus quiet. Introduce children to the class instruments. (If you have none, focus on the rhythm element of this activity.) Discuss the *Scenario guidelines* together. Look at the composition guidance and consider Gertie's tune. Can the class clap it out together? How does it sound on different instruments? Watch the introduction again, and talk to the class about the meanings of 'duration' and 'dynamics':
- **Duration** refers to longer or shorter beats, steady beats, and rhythm.
- **Dynamics** refers to louder or quieter sounds, or silence.

Running the scenario
Arrange the class individually, in pairs or in small groups. Distribute the photocopiables *Animal cards* and *Composition sheet.* **Do not allow children access to the instruments** although they could refer to the photocopiable *Typical percussion instruments.* Encourage children to think about the qualities of their animal, the sort of piece they wish to compose and the instrument they want to use. Once children have created a composition that they are happy with, allow them to try it out very quietly on their chosen instrument. What enhancements might they make?

Differentiation
Less confident learners should work up to eight beats with only one or two instruments.
More confident learners could try more complex arrangements up to 16 beats and beyond. Can they use half-beats?

Review
Gather the class together and discuss each others' compositions on paper. Use this as an opportunity to model key mathematical language: number names; odd/even; and, of course, counting. Ask children to clap out some of the compositions while others count the beats. To conclude, give everyone five minutes to practise, then have them play their pieces.

Further ideas
- Record children's work played several times over (either by repeating it or by digital manipulation of their recordings – quite easily done by adults on most computers.)
- Challenge children to create dance pieces to match their compositions. Listen to *Carnival of the Animals* by Saint-Saëns.

At Rat-a-tat Zoo all the animals love music. It is one of the reasons they are so happy.

Each type of animal would like to have its own tune. Whenever people go to look at them in their enclosures, the tune will play.

But what sort of tunes do they want?

All the animals say they want rhythms that match their personalities. The tunes must only use percussion instruments! Can you help them?

■ Composing for Rat-a-tat Zoo is quite easy.

■ First, choose your instrument or instruments.

Drum with stick	Cymbals	Shakers	Tambourine
Bongo	Triangle	Finger cymbals	Guiro

■ Next, compose your tune.
  ● An empty square means silence.
  ● A small dot means a quiet bang, bash, tap, shake or scrape.
  ● A middle-sized dot means a normal bang, bash, tap, shake or scrape.
  ● A large dot means a loud bang, bash, tap, shake or scrape.

■ This is the tune for Gertie Gorilla:

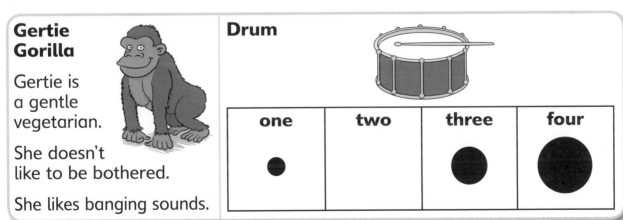

Gertie Gorilla

Gertie is a gentle vegetarian.

She doesn't like to be bothered.

She likes banging sounds.

Drum

one	two	three	four
●		⬤	⬤

■ Imagine how this would sound if you repeated it over and over.

■ Can you try to play or clap the tune?

Bertie Bat

Bats like to sleep all day.

They fly quietly at night.

They sleep hanging upside down!

Edna Elephant

Elephants are big, heavy and very clever.

They love to squirt water.

They can be very loud!

Colin Crocodile

Crocodiles can be lazy.

They like to lie in rivers.

They have very sharp teeth for biting.

Freddie Flamingo

Flamingos have long thin legs and elegant necks.

They are pink.

They often live in huge flocks.

Gertrude Giraffe

Giraffes are usually very quiet and shy.

They have very long bodies.

They can run quickly.

Kevin Kangaroo

Kangaroos can hop a long way.

They have big strong tails.

They carry their babies in a pouch.

Leanne Lion

Most animals are scared of lions.

Lions hunt other animals.

They have a very loud roar.

Melanie Monkey

Monkeys can move quickly.

They swing through the trees.

They love to play and chatter.

Timothy Tarantula

Tarantulas are silent, hairy and scary.

Some tarantulas can hurt you very much if they bite you.

Name(s)

one	two	three	four	five	six	seven	eight

nine	ten	eleven	twelve	thirteen	fourteen	fifteen	sixteen

Red Riding Hood's postal service

Overview
An activity covering a range of early maths objectives through a post office simulation.

Timescales
- Lesson 1 (about 30 minutes): Introduce key concepts and the scenario. Model skills through examples.
- Lesson 2 (various options): Run the session as a whole class or adopt a carousel-based approach.
- Repeating (various options): Create new letter and parcel requirements. Ask children to create their own stamp system, or change the costs.
- Extension: Challenge children to create their own charts using specific measurements and weights for different items, and then operate their own post office using these charts. Use the blank charts and postal records provided on the CD-ROM.

Maths covered
- Colours and shapes.
- Number bonds to 20 (extension to 100).
- Data handling – pictograms.
- Simple money (optional).
- Measuring length and weight (optional).

Prior learning
Children will need a basic familiarity with the mathematical skills involved.

Cross-curricular links
- Literacy: speaking and listening.
- ICT: data handling.

CD-ROM resources list
- Scenario video and slideshow.
- Pictogram tool.
- Photocopiables: *Scenario guidelines, Stamps and charts, Postal records, Blank stamps and charts, Extension charts and stamps, Blank postal records.*

Resource list
Coloured pens/pencils, scissors, glue sticks.

Setting the scene
Watch the introduction on the CD-ROM, which explains post rooms, stamps, and Red Riding Hood's delivery service.

Discuss children's understanding of post offices, the postal system, and stamps. Look at the photocopiable *Scenario guidelines* together and work through some examples with the children. (The delivery options chart is for more confident learners.) Ensure that they know how to record transactions on the *Postal records* photocopiable and stick a stamp on the right-hand side. (The last three tasks on *Postal records* involve delivery options.)

Running the scenario
There are several ways to organise this activity:
- Running the activity as a whole class lesson is easiest, using photocopiable *Postal records*. This requires less 'role play' than the carousel option below, but gives you the opportunity to have all children using the skills involved simultaneously.
- Running the activity with a carousel approach can be very effective, especially for children who need more concrete reinforcement. Children take turns to work in pairs behind a post office counter. Throughout a session, the remaining children break off their other tasks to go to the 'post office' and submit a letter or parcel for posting. Over several days it should be possible for all of the class to experience this set-up.

Differentiation
Less confident learners could initially focus only on choosing the correct stamps, moving on to the 'role play' based approach explained above.

More confident learners can try the activities that include delivery options. Children might also use photocopiable *Extension charts and stamps* (number bonds to 100).

Review
Work with groups to create pictograms using the tool on the CD-ROM. What does this tell us about the letters and parcels posted that day?

Further ideas
Arrange a visit to your local post or sorting office. Alternatively, ask children to develop a postal system using the coloured stamps to denote different delivery options.

Red Riding Hood has her own post office. She has to provide stamps for all sorts of parcels for all sorts of customers.

Today, she needs help. She has to go to see Grandma in the woods and needs someone to help her. Would you help her with today's customers please?

This is how it works:

- Rumpelstiltskin has a letter to post.
- He would like to send it to London.
- The letter is 10cm wide.
- The chart shows that a 10cm letter is a *small letter*.
- A *small letter* needs a square stamp.
- A square stamp costs 1p.

Rumpelstiltskin's letter needs a square stamp that costs 1p.

Red Riding Hood puts the stamp on Rumpelstiltskin's letter.

She fills in her postal record book like this:

Customer: Rumpelstiltskin   **Letter:** 10cm wide

Destination: London   **Cost:** 1p

Stamp needed

- Your teacher will give you some postal records and might read these out to you.
- Work out the correct stamp for each letter or parcel.

Delivery options

Some customers also want to choose a delivery option.

- Rumpelstiltskin wants to send his letter by *Express delivery*.
- *Express delivery* needs a yellow stamp.
- *Express delivery* has an extra cost of 8p.

Red Riding Hood colours the square stamp yellow.

She works out 1p + 8p = 9p.

She puts the details into her postal records book, as above.

Letter or parcel chart

Letter or parcel	Greatest width and weight	Stamp	
Small letter	up to 15cm wide	square	1p
Large letter	over 15cm wide	circle	3p
Small parcel	up to 3kg	triangle	5p
Large parcel	between 3kg and 10kg	rectangle	7p

Delivery options chart

Delivery options	Delivery time	Stamp	Extra cost
Second class	takes 1 week	red	2p
First class	takes 3 days	blue	4p
Express delivery	next day	yellow	8p
Special delivery	delivered with a song	green	12p

Postal records – Red Riding Hood

Name(s):_____

Customer: Prince Charming

Destination: A princess in London

Letter: 20cm

Cost: _____

Stamp needed

Customer: Mrs Goat

Destination: The troll under the bridge

Parcel: 2kg

Cost: _____

Stamp needed

Customers: Hansel and Gretel

Destination: Their parents

Parcel: 7kg

Cost: _____

Stamp needed

Customer: Humpty Dumpty

Destination: The King

Letter: 12cm

Cost: _____

Stamp needed

Tasks with delivery options

Customer: Rapunzel
Parcel: 1kg **Cost:** ____
Destination: The witch
Delivery: First class **Cost:** ____
Total cost: _____

Stamp needed

Customer: Jill
Letter: 18cm **Cost:** ____
Destination: Jack in hospital
Delivery: Special delivery **Cost:** ____
Total cost: _____

Stamp needed

Pirate birthdays

Overview
Children play three different activities in which they put birthdays in order: days, then months, then ages.

Timescales
- Lesson I (less than I hour): Recap days of the week and months of the year. Introduce the scenario.
- Lesson 2 (about I hour): Complete the activities, either in one session or three shorter sessions.
- Repeating: A second playing of the games will be easier, but can be given a fresh focus by using the photocopiable *Pirate birthdays*, or by replacing the pirate cards with different details (the photocopiable *Blank pirate birthdays* has images only).
- Extension: Challenge more confident children to calculate how long it is, or has been, from today to each pirate's birthday this year.

Maths covered
- Arranging items by days of the week and months of the year.
- Ordering numbers between I and 100.
- Finding differences between dates (extension).

Prior learning
Children should be familiar with the calendar and numbers up to 100.

Cross-curricular links
- Literacy: speaking and listening.
- History: basic chronology.

CD-ROM resources list
- Scenario video and slideshow.
- Photocopiables: *Scenario guidelines*, *Pirate cards*, *Job rotas*, *Who's cooking*, *Who's scrubbing?*, *Who's the lookout?*, *Pirate birthdays*, *Blank pirate birthdays*, *Sharing out the treasure*, *Who's who?*, *Rules for the crew*, *Talking pirate*.

Resource list
Pencils, paper, glue sticks, up-to-date calendar showing days (optional).

Setting the scene
Explain to the class that they will be taking part in activities to organise a crew of pirates for their various jobs on board their ship. For the first lesson an overview of how weeks and calendars are structured may be needed. Watch the introduction to the activities, then follow the on-screen information to organise the pirates. Using a range of days, birthdays and ages (not from the pirate cards) model how each activity works. Model the language of chronology, for example: before, after, next.

Running the scenario
Use the photocopiable *Scenario guidelines* as a script for the activity, and discuss the activities. Arrange the class into groups of two to four children and give each a complete set of cards from the photocopiables *Pirate cards*, *Job rotas*, and the recording photocopiables *Who's cooking*, *Who's scrubbing?* and *Who's the lookout?* (You could enlarge each sheet to A3.) As children work, circulate and ensure everyone is contributing appropriately and that everyone is entering information correctly.

Differentiation
This activity will probably work best if children are grouped by attainment.
Less confident learners can have all the cards showing at the beginning.
More confident learners could be encouraged to complete the extension activities.

Review
Once all the groups have completed their charts, ask groups to check their work by discussing the answers with another group. Try to create a definitive set of charts on the interactive whiteboard.

Further ideas
- Challenge children to create a pirate crew using the dates of birth of their families and friends.
- Create an imaginary pirate ship, complete with rules and rotas, and write about or act life aboard ship.

Ha, har me hearties, welcome to the good ship *Pongalot*! Shiver me timbers and a bottle of pop! Aye, it's a grand life sailing the seven seas with Cap'n Bob, looking for treasure, excitement and adventure. Me and my family of pirates have been plundering treasure for years and years. We have pirates of all ages aboard!

But we needs help to sort out our ship. Things are getting in a bit of a mess. Can you help us to get our ship ship-shape?

- You have to complete three activities.

- You need the charts on the CD-ROM *Who's cooking?*, *Who's scrubbing?* and *Who's the lookout?*

- The same rules apply to each activity.

1. At the start of each activity, shuffle the 16 pirate cards. Share them equally between your group. If there is a card left over, put it face up so that everyone can see it.

2. Each person should hold their cards so that the others can't see them. Your must complete the charts by talking about your cards, not showing them.

3. Take it in turns to talk about one of your cards. If everyone agrees that the card they have described **is the next one to go on the chart**, you can write the details down, or stick the card down.

Example

A group of four children are completing the rota for cooking.

They have shared the cards out.

They have decided who will go first.

Sun	Mon	Tue	Wed	Thur	Fri	Sat

First child: 'I don't have anyone whose birthday is on a Sunday.'

[They all agree not to do anything.]

Second child: 'I have Knock-kneed Neville. He was born on Sunday.'

[They all agree to put Neville down on the rota for Sunday.]

Third child: 'I have Nervous Nelly. She was also born on Sunday.'

[They all agree to put Nelly down on the rota for Sunday too.]

Fourth child: 'I don't have anyone whose birthday is on a Sunday.'

[They all agree not to do anything.]

After another brief round, they will agree that no one else has a crew member born on a Sunday. The conversation should then move to Monday, and so on.

Bonkers Boris

Born on: Tuesday

Birthday: 1st October

Age: 21 years old

Crazy Cleo

Born on: Thursday

Birthday: 3rd June

Age: 64 years old

Dirty Dave

Born on: Monday

Birthday: 20th June

Age: 24 years old

Evil Edna

Born on: Saturday

Birthday: 22nd August

Age: 42 years old

Fearless Freda

Born on: Monday

Birthday: 5th July

Age: 97 years old

Greedy Gary

Born on: Thursday

Birthday: 23rd September

Age: 50 years old

Horrible Hilda

Born on: Friday

Birthday: 11th March

Age: 57 years old

Knock-kneed Neville

Born on: Sunday

Birthday: 27th January

Age: 18 years old

Mad Mike

Born on: Friday

Birthday: 21st September

Age: 30 years old

Nervous Nelly

Born on: Sunday

Birthday: 24th November

Age: 46 years old

Pongy Pam

Born on: Saturday

Birthday: 17th July

Age: 19 years old

Rotten Ruby

Born on: Tuesday

Birthday: 14th March

Age: 90 years old

Stinky Stephen

Born on: Wednesday

Birthday: 27th November

Age: 77 years old

Terrible Tina

Born on: Tuesday

Birthday: 11th April

Age: 41 years old

Warty Wilma

Born on: Wednesday

Birthday: 7th May

Age: 37 years old

Zany Zac

Born on: Thursday

Birthday: 2nd February

Age: 28 years old

Job rotas — Pirate birthdays

Activity 1   Who's cooking?

Work out the ship's **daily** cooking rota.

- Put pirates on the same day as their birthday.
- Fill in the rota in the correct order. Sunday is first.

Feast!

- If three or more pirates cook on the same day, there is a feast.
- Tick the days that will have a feast.

Activity 2   Who's scrubbing?

Work out the ship's **weekly** cleaning rota.

- Put pirates on the same month as their birthday.
- Fill in the rota in the correct order. January is first.

Polish the treasure!

- If more than one pirate cleans in the same month, they will polish Cap'n Bob's treasure.
- Tick the months when the treasure is polished.

Activity 3   Who's the lookout?

Work out the ship's lookout rota by ordering dates of birth. Decide who goes in the crow's nest.

- Each pirate must spend one hour in the crow's nest.
- Put pirates in order of their age, starting with the youngest.
- Fill in the rota in the correct order.

A big day out

Overview

Children plan a trip around a town, using a map to help them.

Timescales

- Lesson 1 (less than 1 hour): Introduce the event and the concepts. Model language and guidelines through examples.
- Lesson 2 (about 1 hour): Run the day and check workings.
- Repeating: Repeat the game, either at a harder level, or using different starting points or routes.
- Extension: Challenge more confident children to find the fastest possible route to visit all the shops and café.

Maths covered

- Directions/turns.
- Simple coordinates.
- Distances (optional).
- Adding time (optional).

Prior learning

Children should be familiar with simple maps and directions.

Cross-curricular links

- Literacy: speaking and listening.
- Geography: reading simple maps and keys.

CD-ROM resources list

- Scenario video and slideshow.
- Photocopiables: *Scenario guidelines*, *Map of Tinytown*, *Tina Ted's journey planning sheet*, *A big day out*, *Tinytown challenge*, *Blank grid*.

Resource list

Pencils, counters, small toy for Tina (optional).

Setting the scene

Watch the introduction on the CD-ROM and look at the map of Tinytown with the class. Discuss examples of planning routes on the map, paying particular attention to the key and conventions for recording coordinates. Look at the *Scenario guidelines* together, and model appropriate language through the example journey (*forward, right turn* and *left turn*.)

Demonstrate how the destination then becomes the starting point for the next leg of the journey. If appropriate, talk about the 'shorthand' version for route planning. Remind children that turning right or left is relative to the direction Tina is facing. Discuss further sample routes as required, using the colour map on the photocopiable *A big day out* on your interactive whiteboard.

Running the scenario

It is imperative before running the scenario that you decide which children will be doing which activity. Organise the class individually or in pairs as desired, and distribute the photocopiables *Map of Tinytown* and *Tina Ted's journey planning sheet*. If preferred, the activity can be undertaken by displaying the colour map on the photocopiable *A big day out* on your interactive whiteboard. Encourage children to use a counter with a direction arrow marked on it, or the cut-out picture of Tina on the recording sheet, to help them.

Differentiation

Less confident learners can do the easier activities. If writing directions is too difficult, it is enough for children to trace routes on the map with their fingers, draw the route, or simply state it for someone else to map.

More confident learners can do the harder activities.

Review

Discuss what children found most difficult about this activity. Was it keeping track of multiple instructions, or perhaps keeping a clear head about which way was right or left? Choose children to read their directions, and ask the class to follow their route.

Further ideas

- Challenge children to play the game on the photocopiable *Tinytown challenge*.
- Ask children to hide their maps and take turns to give directions to each other. Do they both end up at the same shop?
- Use the *Blank grid* photocopiable to create a new version of the game.

Welcome to Tinytown, the home of Tina Ted!

There are nine shops and a café in Tinytown. Tina has to work out the fastest route around town. Can you help her to plan her shopping route and get her back to a bus stop?

There are four bus stops to choose from. Some shops have more than one entrance. It is okay to go in by one door and leave by another. Write clear instructions for Tina. Good luck!

There are five different ways to play "A big day out".

1. **Where are the shops?**
   - Choose three shops.
   - Give their positions on the grid. For example, the bike shop is at E7.

2. **Bus stop to shop**
   - Choose a bus stop and a shop.
   - Give the route from the bus stop to the shop.

3. **Shop to shop**
   - Choose two shops.
   - Give the route from one shop to the other shop.

4. **A quick day out**
   - Choose a starting position and three shops.
   - Can you plan a route for Tina to do her shopping?

5. **A big day out**
   - Choose a starting position.
   - Can you plan a route for Tina to visit every shop?
   - If you have time, can you get her back to where she started?

Example

Start		Directions	Destination	
Bus stop 1, square D1		Forward 1 square to D2, turn left, forward 1 square to C2.	The hat shop, square C2	
The hat shop, square C2		Forward 2 squares to E2, turn right, forward 1 square to E1.	The scarf shop, square E1	

Writing in shorthand

Start		Directions	Destination	
Bus stop 1 square D1		FD1, LT, FD1	The hat shop, square C2	
The hat shop, square C2		FD2, RT, FD1	The scarf shop, square E1	

Key

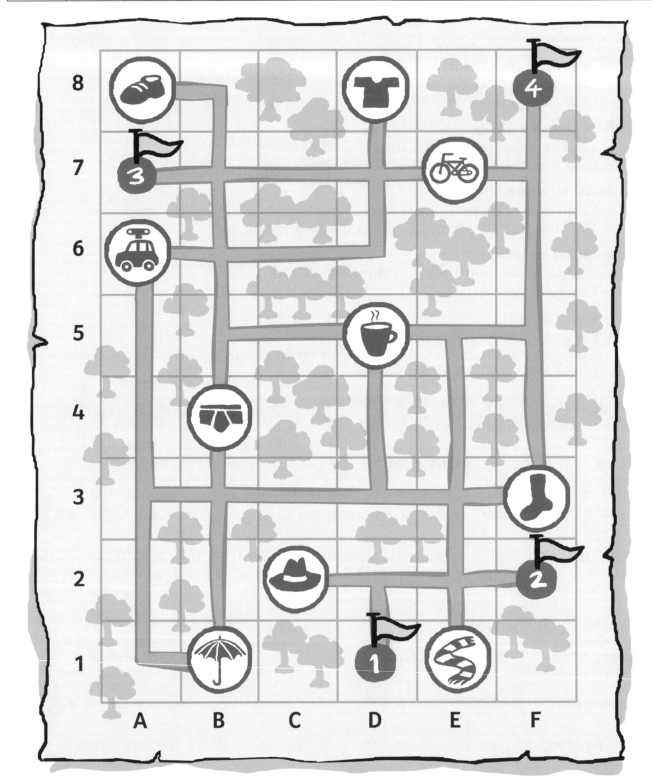										
Shoe shop	Clothes shop	Bike shop	Toy shop	Café	Under-wear shop	Sock shop	Umbrella shop	Hat shop	Scarf shop	Bus stops

Name(s):_____

■ Cut out this picture of Tina. Use it to help you plan your route.

Start	Directions	Destination

■ If you need to write more directions, use another sheet.

Playground champs

Overview

Children take part in a virtual sports day, monitoring competitors' progress through a range of activities.

Timescales

- Lesson 1 (30 minutes): Introduce the events and the scoring system.
- Lesson 2 (60 minutes): Complete all events and then check one another's work. Calculate final scores and decide on the winners.
- Repeating: Competitor's results change each time you use the CD-ROM. Try reducing calculation time to increase the challenge.
- Extension: Give children the photocopiable *Sample data* for all six competitors. Challenge them to calculate the final points for all competitors and calculate team points.

Maths covered

- Understanding place value.
- Adding tens.
- Cardinal and ordinal numbers (one, two, three; first, second, third).

Prior learning

Children will need prior familiarity with place value and adding tens.

Cross-curricular links

PE: sport awareness.

CD-ROM resources list

- Scenario video and slideshow.
- On-screen results generator.
- Photocopiables: *Scenario guidelines, Score card, Sample data, Winning positions.*

Resource list

Pencils and paper.

Setting the scene

Show children the introductory animation on the CD-ROM. Discuss their understanding of sports days and the difference between competitive events and personal progress. Explain to the class that they will take part in a virtual sports day, choosing a competitor and following their progress.

Display the *Scenario guidelines* and talk through the activities and how points are calculated. Work through the examples, in particular pointing out for the racing events that the lower the number the better the performance. Distribute the photocopiable *Score card* and talk through how it works. Focus on child improvement for the second try and how this provides additional points.

Running the scenario

Arrange children individually, in pairs or small groups. Either allow them to choose a competitor, or assign them. Start the events on your interactive whiteboard. (Use the photocopiable *Sample data* if you do not have access to an interactive whiteboard.) As the activity runs, check that children are comfortable calculating points for each event, pausing as required. Also check that children identify the winning order for each activity correctly. Once all six events have been completed, children should check one another's calculations. Children who have been monitoring the same competitor can check one another's work. Move on to the second tries. Remind children that competitors score an extra 30 points for improved performance. Finally, children total their points for both tries. Once work has been checked, as a class compile an overall points table. Which children followed the winner?

Differentiation

Less confident learners should use pencil and paper methods or equipment to support their calculations. **More confident learners** can be challenged to calculate all scores mentally.

Review

Ask children if they found the points system difficult. Can they suggest a different system? (The obvious system is one point for first, two for second… and the lowest total wins.)

Further ideas

Children could plan an actual 'playground champs' day of their own, either for themselves or for younger children, using events of their choice and a suitable points system for each event.

Scenario guidelines — Playground champs

- There are six activities for developing your "playground champ" skills.

Cone jumping
How many cones can you jump over?

One-leg balance
For how long can you stand on one leg?

Star jumps
How many star jumps can you do in 30 seconds?

Hopping race
How fast can you hop 20 metres?

High jump
How high can you jump?

Beanbag-balance race
How fast can you run 30 metres with a beanbag on your head?

Scoring points

Position	First	Second	Third	Fourth	Fifth	Sixth
Points	60	50	40	30	20	10

- If two people tie, they both get the points, and no one gets the points below them.
- For the second try, if anyone improves on their first try they get an extra 30 points.

Example

First try	Rashid	Beth	Hanmo	Kelvin	Aleesha	Sam
Cone jumping (number of cones)	9	4	5	8	6	5

Second try	Rashid	Beth	Hanmo	Kelvin	Aleesha	Sam
Cone jumping (number of cones)	6	5	6	10	7	8

On the first try, Rashid jumped over nine cones. He was first. He scores 60 points.
On the first try, Beth jumped over four cones. She was sixth. She scores 10 points.
On the first try, Sam and Hanmo were joint fourth. They get 30 points each, and nobody is fifth.

On the second try, Rashid jumped over six cones. He was joint fourth but he did not improve. He scores 30 points.
On the second try, Beth jumped over five cones. She was sixth and she did improve. She scores 10 + 30 = 40 points.
On the second try, Beth, Hanmo, Kelvin, Aleesha and Sam all improved. They all get an extra 30 points.

Name(s):_____ **Competitor:**_____

First try:

Activity	Result	Position	Points
Cone jumping			
One-leg balance			
Star jumps			
Hopping race			
High jump			
Beanbag-balance race			
Total points			

Second try:

Remember

- For the hopping and beanbag races, a smaller time is an improvement.
- For all the others, a higher result is better.

Activity	Result	Position	Improved? Add 30 points	Total Points
Cone jumping				
One-leg balance				
Star jumps				
Hopping race				
High jump				
Beanbag-balance race				
Total points				

Total points for both tries = _____ + _____ = _____

Sample data — Playground champs

This data has been provided for those who do not have access to an interactive whiteboard. The data below are the results for six competitors.

Please note that the software on the CD-ROM provides more variety, as all competitors' scores are calculated randomly every time the software is used.

First try:

Activities	Competitors					
	Rashid	**Beth**	**Hanmo**	**Kelvin**	**Aleesha**	**Sam**
Cone jumping (number of cones)	9	4	5	8	6	5
One-leg balance (number of seconds)	15	17	12	18	6	7
Star jumps in 30 seconds (number of jumps)	10	13	25	17	12	17
Hopping race (number of seconds)	21	31	27	22	24	31
High jump (number of centimetres)	38	29	39	29	30	33
Beanbag-balance race (number of seconds)	45	37	36	44	33	33

Second try:

Activities	Competitors					
	Rashid	**Beth**	**Hanmo**	**Kelvin**	**Aleesha**	**Sam**
Cone jumping (number of cones)	6	5	6	10	7	8
One-leg balance (number of seconds)	15	12	12	18	10	18
Star jumps in 30 seconds (number of jumps)	12	23	24	18	11	14
Hopping race (number of seconds)	28	29	32	26	32	25
High jump (number of centimetres)	25	39	30	30	27	32
Beanbag-balance race (number of seconds)	37	41	43	49	38	47

Magical mosaics

Overview
Children design mosaics according to specified requirements.

Timescales
- Lesson 1 (about 1 hour): Introduce the concepts and work through some examples.
- Lesson 2 (1 hour minimum): Children design a specific mosaic, list materials and then calculate costs (optional).
- Further lessons: Children design a range of mosaics and then calculate costs (optional).
- Extension: Children devise their own requirements, creating free-form mosaic designs that are not based around a grid, and then calculate costs.

Maths covered
- Understanding shape, symmetry, counting.
- Multiplication or counting in 2s, 5s and 10s to calculate costs.

Prior learning
Children need an understanding of shape and symmetry, and multiplying or counting in 2s, 5s and 10s.

Cross-curricular links
Art: creating designs.

CD-ROM resources list
- Scenario video and slideshow.
- Photocopiables: *Scenario guidelines*, *Customer request sheet*, *Design proposal sheet*, *Planning grid and prices*, *Customer requests 1 and 2*, *Customer requests 3 and 4*.

Resource list
Pencils, coloured pencils, pens, paper, squared paper, rulers, counters or interlocking cubes for support.

Setting the scene
Show children the video and photo slideshow about making mosaics on the CD-ROM. Discuss their understanding of mosaics and consider how they are made. Explain that they will be making mosaics for different customers. Talk through the photocopiable *Scenario guidelines* and discuss how children should plan and present their work. If necessary, remind children what symmetry is. Discuss how they might calculate the cost of some tiles. Work through examples with the class.

Running the scenario
Arrange the children individually, in pairs or small groups and give each group the customer request of your choice. (Photocopiables *Customer requests 1 and 2* and *Customer requests 3 and 4* have grids drawn to size so children can focus on their designs.) Everyone might have the same design so you can compare work, or different groups might have different designs.

Before copying the photocopiables *Customer requests 1 and 2*, *Customer requests 3 and 4* and *Design proposal sheet*, enter suitable prices for each tile. An example price structure is given on *Planning grid and prices*.

Provide copies of the grid from the photocopiable *Planning grid and prices* (or use squared paper.) Initially, ask children to spend time brainstorming ideas and discussing issues. Encourage them to consider carefully the customer requirements.

Differentiation
Less confident learners might work only on smaller designs, counting tiles required but omitting costs.
More confident learners can develop more complex designs, leading to accurate listings of materials and ultimately calculating the cost of their mosaic.

Review
Ask children to share their work with each other, and then have one or more groups present to the class. Have groups created the mosaic requested? Are children's calculations for material requirements accurate? Is the work clearly presented and easy to understand? Would the customers like their designs?

Further ideas
- Create models of children's mosaics using coloured paper, interlocking cubes, beads or circular counters.
- Create a commission for your own mosaic, perhaps for a particular room or person, and design it.

You are going to be working in Magical Mosaics. This is a shop that designs and makes small mosaics for different customers. It is a very busy shop and is famous for making the best mosaics. Can you design new ones that your customers will love? Remember, they will only ask you to make a real mosaic if they like the designs you make, and if the cost is right!

Planning a mosaic

- Read or listen to the customer's requests carefully.

- Think about what colours you are going to use.

- Check that you know where the centre and edges of your mosaic will be.

Simple mosaics

These simple mosaics have no colour.
What colours would you use?

Symmetry

A symmetrical pattern is when one part is like a mirror image to the other.

Examples are a butterfly and a person's face.

With mosaics you can create very precise symmetrical patterns. Look at where the lines of symmetry are in these mosaics:

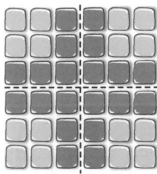

Tips for effective working

- If possible, try to look at as many mosaics as possible before you start.

- Try sketching lots of ideas in rough and experiment with different colours.

- If you are working in a group, make sure everyone has something to do, and that you all agree on your plans.

■ Here are the latest requests from customers who came into Magical Mosaics:

<table>
<tr>
<td rowspan="3">Straightforward designs</td>
<td>1</td>
<td>■ A square mosaic.
■ 4 tiles wide and 4 tiles high.</td>
<td>■ Use 2 colours.</td>
</tr>
<tr>
<td>2</td>
<td>■ A square mosaic.
■ 6 tiles wide and 6 tiles high.</td>
<td>■ Use 3 colours.
■ It must be stripy.</td>
</tr>
<tr>
<td>3</td>
<td>■ A square mosaic.
■ 6 tiles wide and 6 tiles high.
■ Use up to 4 colours.</td>
<td>■ It must have a cross in it.</td>
</tr>
<tr>
<td rowspan="3">More complex designs involving symmetry</td>
<td>4</td>
<td>■ A square mosaic.
■ 8 tiles wide and 8 tiles high.
■ Use up to 6 colours.</td>
<td>■ It must have a border around the outside and a pattern in the middle.
■ It must be symmetrical.</td>
</tr>
<tr>
<td>5</td>
<td>■ A rectangular mosaic.
■ 10 tiles wide and 4 tiles high.
■ Use up to 4 colours.</td>
<td>■ It must have 2 lines of symmetry.</td>
</tr>
<tr>
<td>6</td>
<td>■ A square mosaic.
■ 16 tiles wide and 16 tiles high.
■ Use up to 4 colours.</td>
<td>■ It must have a diagonal line of symmetry.
■ Remember, you can cut tiles in half if you need to.</td>
</tr>
<tr>
<td rowspan="3">Open ideas for greater creativity</td>
<td>7</td>
<td>■ Make a large rectangular mosaic for someone who loves football.
■ It can be any size.</td>
<td>■ You can use half-tiles if you need to, and as many colours as you like.</td>
</tr>
<tr>
<td>8</td>
<td>■ Make a square mosaic for someone who loves flowers.
■ It can be any size.</td>
<td>■ You can use half-tiles if you need to, and as many colours as you like.</td>
</tr>
<tr>
<td>9</td>
<td>■ Make a mosaic for someone who loves the seaside.
■ It can be any size.</td>
<td>■ You can use half-tiles if you need to, and as many colours as you like.</td>
</tr>
</table>

Design proposal sheet — Magical mosaics

Name(s):_____

Tiles	Number used	Cost per tile	Calculation	Cost
Black				
Red				
Green				
Yellow				
Blue				
Orange				
			Total cost	

Shopalot

Overview
Children take on the roles of stallholders and shoppers.

Timescales
- Lesson 1 (hour maximum): Introduce indoor markets and the skills needed. Prepare the scenario.
- Lesson 2 (about 1 hour): Run a day in the market: some children set up their stalls and others go shopping.
- Lesson 3 (about 1 hour): Run through the 'day' again with children in different roles.
- Extension: Challenge shoppers to total up their day's spending, and stallholders to calculate their profits.

Maths covered
- Mental maths using known facts/bonds to £20; adding to £100 (optional).
- Money: whole pounds only – £1 coins and £5 and £10 notes.

Cross-curricular links
- Literacy: speaking and listening.
- D&T: logo design; clothes design.
- PSHE: financial awareness.

CD-ROM resources list
- Scenario video and slideshow.
- Photocopiables: *Scenario guidelines, Stall goods, Character templates, Goods for additional stalls, Shopalot money, Stallholders' headband and shoppers' wallets, Money recording sheet.*

Resource list
Pencils, colouring pencils, paper, glue sticks, paper money and plastic pound coins (optional).

Setting the scene
Watch the introduction on the CD-ROM and discuss the scenario with the class. Explain that children will set up stalls, and shop to buy items for two characters. Discuss the key skills involved, and model interactions between stallholders and customers. If desired, demonstrate how to make a note of takings and spending.

Look at the stallholders' goods (on the photocopiable *Stall goods* and extra items on *Goods for additional stalls* if

desired). Talk through the *Scenario guidelines* and discuss pricing considerations, for example that better quality goods cost more.
Distribute the goods in suitable amounts. Initially, everyone should create a stall. At your discretion, use the photocopiables *Stallholders' headband and shoppers' wallets.*

For Lesson 1, half the class will be stallholders and the remainder shoppers, with roles reversed for the next lesson (preferably on a different day). The activity works best if there are several of the same type of stall in each lesson.

Running the scenario
Arrange the classroom – there will be lots of movement. Choose who will be stallholders for Lesson 1, and who will be customers (you may want children to work individually or in pairs). Remind shoppers that they must get the best value for money possible – they must 'shop around'. Ensure that everyone has enough money and that you have a good supply of change (not additional money) should children need it. If appropriate, you could introduce 'haggling' into the role play. Provide shoppers with glue sticks so they can "dress" their characters.

Differentiation
More confident learners should be encouraged to do all calculations mentally.
Less confident learners should work in pairs, and/or have access to calculation aids.

Review
Ask children to add up their takings or to check their purchases and left-over money. Who made a good profit? Who is happy with their purchases? Discuss how the 'day' unfolded. Would children act differently next time?

Further ideas
- Interview stallholders. What are the key maths skills in their work?
- Involve children in planning, preparing and running an actual bring-and-buy sale in school.

Welcome to Shopalot, home of the famous Shopalot Market. Here, you can buy all sorts of clothing and bits and pieces, all at great prices.

Whether you are a stallholder or a shopper, it's always fun to shop in Shopalot!

Setting up a stall

- Each stall sells only one type of item, such as hats.
- Your teacher will tell you what sort of stall you are running, and how many items you have to start.
- Write prices on or next to all the things you are selling.
- You can sell your goods for any price you want, as long as the price is in exact pounds. (For example, £10.50 isn't allowed.)
- You start with a 'float' of five £1 coins.
- If you run out of change, your teacher can help.

Shoppers

- You are buying for two characters. Can you give them names?
- You have £45 to spend.
- Buy one of each item for your two characters.
- Try to get the best possible value for money. Also choose some nice items for them.
- Look after your money carefully. Use a wallet or a container.
- Dress your characters with everything you buy for them.

- Teachers: You will need multiple copies of this sheet, depending on how many children are in your class.

- Each stall should have between 16 and 24 items to sell, which is 4 to 6 of each of the four types of goods.

- Remember to add prices to each item. Colour and cut round the goods if you have time.

You are running a shoe stall

 *

 **

 ***

 ****

You are running a hat stall

 *

 **

 ***

 ****

You are running a scarf stall

 *

 **

 ***

 ****

You are running an umbrella stall

 *

 **

 ***

 ****

You are running a sock stall

 *

 **

 ***

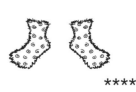 ****

Name(s): _____

Frieda's Fruit Farm

Overview
Children buy and sell berries. Buying requires multiple-calculations. Selling involves checking prices and giving change.

Timescales
- Lesson 1 (less than 1 hour): Introduce the scenario and practise the skills needed.
- Lesson 2 (about 1 hour): Run a 'day' at Frieda's Fruit Farm, check money spent and received.
- Repeating (about 1 hour): Run through the 'day' again, giving children different tasks or roles.
- Extension: Challenge children to create their own shopping lists, food stalls and price lists.

Maths covered
- Times tables.
- Adding and subtracting money.
- Organising number work for longer tasks.

Cross-curricular links
- Literacy: speaking and listening.
- PSHE: healthy eating; financial awareness.

CD-ROM resources list
- Scenario video and slideshow.
- Photocopiables: *Scenario guidelines, Berry price list, Shopping planning sheet, Berries, Coins.*

Resource list
Pencils, paper, plastic money (optional), containers for carrying money and 'goods'.

Setting the scene
Watch the introduction on the CD-ROM and discuss the scenario. Using the berry prices provides times-tables practice. Look at the photocopiable *Berry price list* and discuss an example shopping list. Emphasise how children can choose berries but they must not buy more than they can afford. Work through an example shopping plan, modelling good practice for laying out work, and the calculations needed. Begin with an easy situation, for example buying one berry for each day of the week, and multiplying to find out the total cost. Also enact some transactions with berry sellers.

Running the scenario
Distribute the photocopiables *Berry price list* and *Shopping planning sheet*. Give each child an appropriate shopping list. You may want children to work in pairs. Children will also need toy money and something to carry the paper fruit in, if they will be actually trading. Initially, all children prepare to go shopping. Once they have planned their lists, assign some to be assistants in the farm shop. Decide whether each assistant sells only one type of berry or more. You can simply have one or two berry stalls and have children approach them 'carousel-style', one or two at a time in-between working on other tasks. Remember to give berry sellers enough fruit and change to supply all the shoppers they might meet.

Differentiation
(Note that the shopping lists are differentiated.)
Less confident learners should work in pairs, and/or have access to calculation aids.
More confident learners should do all calculations mentally. Children may want to do more than one shopping plan as there is enough space on the *Shopping planning sheet*.

Review
Ask children to total their money or to check their purchases and left-over money. Does everyone have the right money? Discuss what might make the activity easier or harder.

Further ideas
- Interview shopkeepers and stallholders about the maths they use.
- Ask children to make their own price lists and shopping lists for other healthy foods and try the activity with these.

Welcome to Frieda's Fruit Farm! Anyone can come to pick their own berries.

(Teachers: Choose suitable lists and distribute. Should you wish, there is room for two lists on the planning sheets.)

Berry shopping lists

Standard lists (focus = 2, 5 and 10-times tables)	Tricky lists (focus = 3, 4 and 5-times tables)
Buy enough berries for **four days**. You only like elderberries, raspberries and strawberries. You have **two berries** for a snack each day. You have **50p** to spend.	Buy enough berries for **five days**. You only like cranberries, bilberries and raspberries. You have **two berries** for a snack each day. You have **40p** to spend.
Buy enough berries for **four days**. You only like elderberries, raspberries and strawberries. You have **four berries** for a snack each day. You have **£1** to spend.	Buy enough berries for **five days**. You only like cranberries, bilberries and raspberries. You have **four berries** for a snack each day. You have **80p** to spend.
Buy enough berries for **four days**. You only like elderberries, raspberries and strawberries. You have **six berries** for a snack each day. You have **£1.50** to spend.	Buy enough berries for **five days**. You only like cranberries, bilberries and raspberries. You have **six berries** for a snack each day. You have **£1.20** to spend.
Buy enough berries for **four days**. You only like elderberries, raspberries and strawberries. You have **eight berries** each day. You have **£2** to spend.	Buy enough berries for **five days**. You only like cranberries, bilberries and raspberries. You have **eight berries** each day. You have **£1.60** to spend.

Hard lists (focus = 3 to 9-times tables)

Buy enough berries for **seven** days. You like all berries except raspberries and strawberries. You eat **six berries** each day. You have **£3** to spend.	Buy enough berries for **seven** days. You like all berries except raspberries and strawberries. You eat **thirty berries** each day. You have **£20** to spend.
Buy enough berries for **seven** days. You like all berries except raspberries and strawberries. You eat **eight berries** each day. You have **£4** to spend.	Buy enough berries for **seven** days. You like all berries except raspberries and strawberries. You eat **thirty berries** each day. You have **£20** to spend.

Elderberries
Delicious in drinks

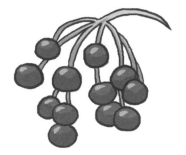

2p each

Cranberries
Ideal for juices

3p each

Bilberries
A tasty snack

4p each

Raspberries
Great with ice cream

5p each

Blackberries
Lovely in pies

6p each

Loganberries
Big and juicy

7p each

Gooseberries
Yummy in tarts

8p each

Blueberries
Fantastic in muffins

9p each

Strawberries
Perfect with cream

10p each

Shopping planning sheet — Frieda's Fruit Farm

Name(s):_____

■ Write or stick your berry shopping list here:

Day	Write down which berries you are going to buy and how much they will cost.
1.	
2.	
3.	
4.	
5.	
6.	
7.	

■ Calculate the total cost here:

Total cost = _____

On safari

Overview
Children find out about wildlife around an African watering hole, and create a written presentation.

Timescales
- Lesson 1 (about 1 hour): Introduce the scenario. Children plan their work.
- Lesson 2 (about 1 hour): Children create their presentations.
- Lesson 3 (various options): Children deliver and discuss their work.
- Extension: Work with partners or adults to research one or more animals in greater depth.

Maths covered
- Estimating.
- Understanding units of length and weight.
- Working with larger numbers.
- Creating charts and diagrams.

Prior learning
- Experience of estimating and of numbers over 100 would be useful.
- Prior awareness of Africa, its location and key facts, would also be beneficial, as would experience of presenting information in different formats.

Cross-curricular links
- Literacy: speaking and listening; reading; writing.
- Science: living things.
- ICT: data handling.

CD-ROM resources list
- Scenario video and slideshow.
- Chart, tally chart, Carroll diagram and pictogram tools.
- Photocopiables: *Scenario guidelines, Animal fact sheet, Safari recording sheet, Useful links and info.*

Resource list
Pencils, paper, books about African wildlife or internet access (optional).

Setting the scene
Explain to the class that they will be going on a virtual safari in a part of Africa. Initially, spend time looking at the photocopiable *Scenario guidelines*, ideally on your interactive whiteboard. Discuss the task with the class, considering how different ways of presenting information are used.

Look at the photocopiable *Animal fact sheet* together and ensure that children can use the chart. (Note: figures may vary from other sources. These are generalised for use in this scenario.) Can they make some simple deductions from it? For example, elephants are the heaviest animal. Ensure that children understand the key focus of the task, and that they appreciate the use of diagrams and charts to help visualise information.

Running the scenario
Arrange the children individually, in pairs or small groups as desired, and distribute the photocopiables *Animal fact sheet* and *Safari recording sheet*. Ask them to decide what they would like their presentations to be about: for example, comparing three animals and ordering their weights, heights and lifespans. Watch the video at least twice to allow children to make notes and/or count the animals. For the larger groups of animals, point out that children will need to estimate numbers. (Ask children to compare estimates, then pause the video and make a more accurate estimate.) Ask children first to plan their presentations and then to create them.

Differentiation
Children's presentations will be differentiated largely by outcome.
Less confident learners compare only two animals, saying which one lives longer, and so on.
More confident learners use written methods to calculate comparisons more accurately, and produce appropriate graphs or charts.

Review
In reviewing children's presentations, consider whether they chose appropriate ways of presenting their information. Does the presentation help us to understand things more easily. Could it be extended to include other animals not yet seen?

Further ideas
Conduct further research into other animals in other habitats. (See photocopiable *Useful links and info* for links to interesting websites.)

Out of Africa

Have you ever heard of Africa? It is a very large continent. It has many different countries and people, lots of whom live in big cities. Africa is hot in many parts, and there is a lot of desert, rainforest and jungle.

You are going to visit the Etosha National Park in Namibia. Can you see it on the map?

There are thousands of wild animals in the Etosha National Park. Be sure to make notes about what you see there!

Etosha

Choosing things to compare

- How many you saw
- Colour
- Describing words
- Size
- Weight
- Lifespan

How can you compare animals?

- Arranging them in order
- Carroll diagrams
- Bar charts
- Scale drawings

Types of presentation

- Magazine or newspaper article
- Website
- Fact files
- Poster

When you are working

- Try to use books or the internet to find out other facts about your chosen animals.
- Think about how you will present your work to the whole class.
- If you are working in groups, make sure you divide the work fairly.

Lion

Height: 100cm

Weight: 160kg

Lifespan: 15 years

Diet: carnivore

Elephant

Height: 350cm

Weight: 5000kg

Lifespan: 60 years

Diet: herbivore

Rhinoceros

Height: 150cm

Weight: 1500kg

Lifespan: 40 years

Diet: herbivore

Zebra

Height: 130cm

Weight: 320kg

Lifespan: 25 years

Diet: herbivore

Springbok

Height: 70cm

Weight: 45kg

Lifespan: 9 years

Diet: herbivore

Hyena

Height: 80cm

Weight: 45kg

Lifespan: 12 years

Diet: carnivore

Wildebeest

Height: 140cm

Weight: 200kg

Lifespan: 17 years

Diet: herbivore

Giraffe

Height: 530cm

Weight: 1200kg

Lifespan: 25 years

Diet: herbivore

Jackal

Height: 40cm

Weight: 12kg

Lifespan: 10 years

Diet: carnivore

Kudu

Height: 130cm

Weight: 250kg

Lifespan: 15 years

Diet: herbivore

Impala

Height: 80cm

Weight: 45kg

Lifespan: 10 years

Diet: herbivore

Oryx

Height: 120cm

Weight: 200kg

Lifespan: 18 years

Diet: herbivore

Safari recording sheet — On safari

- Use this chart to make notes on some of the animals you will see on your classroom safari.

Animal	Colour	Describing words	How many did you see?
Lion			
Elephant			
Rhinoceros			
Zebra			
Springbok			
Hyena			
Wildebeest			
Giraffe			
Jackal			
Kudu			
Impala			
Oryx			

Your presentation

- Write here what type of work you will do.
- What will it be about? What information will it contain?

Gloria's Glorious Gardens

Overview
Using guidelines, price lists and plans, children design and cost a garden.

Timescales
- Lesson 1 (about 1 hour): Introduce concepts and consider skills needed and approaches to presenting work. Work through examples as appropriate.
- Lesson 2 (minimum 1 hour): Children fully design, cost and present a garden of their own.
- Further lessons (minimum 1 hour): Children design and cost gardens for customers.
- Extension: Children research actual costs for items from brochures and design new gardens accordingly.

Maths covered
- Multiplying by 2, 3, 4, 5 and by 10, 20, 30 and 40.
- Adding HTU in the context of money.
- Simple scale and measuring.

Prior learning
Children should be comfortable with extended tasks that need careful organisation.

Cross-curricular links
- Literacy: speaking and listening.
- D&T: design.
- PSHE: financial awareness.

CD-ROM resources list
- Scenario video and slideshow.
- Photocopiables: *Scenario guidelines, Garden supplies price list, Garden design sheet, Garden planning grid, Customer profiles, Customer requests 1 and 2, Customer requests 3 and 4.*
- *Yes/No interactive.*

Resource list
Pencils, paper, rulers, calculators (optional).

Setting the scene
Open the CD-ROM on your interactive whiteboard to let the children meet Gloria and see a range of images. Explain to the class that their task will be to redesign one or more gardens. Finish by looking together at the photocopiables *Scenario guidelines* and *Garden supplies list.* Discuss, model and review the different maths skills involved as appropriate and the desired approach to laying out work by working through the example in the photocopiable *Scenario guidelines.*

Running the scenario
Arrange the children individually, in pairs, or small groups and give each the photocopiables *Garden supplies price list* and *Garden design sheet* (or *Garden planning grid*). Make sure the photocopiable *Scenario guidelines* is available either on the interactive whiteboard or as a photocopiable per group. As children start to work, encourage them to ensure that they have included every item before starting on their calculations. Remind children of the importance of the layout of their work – both when designing and showing calculations for costs.

Differentiation
If you have mixed attainment groups, you can assign roles accordingly.
Less confident learners should focus on the easier gardens. They can also be guided to use items that have rounded prices.
More confident learners could design a garden for one of Gloria's customers. See the photocopiables *Customer profiles, Customer requests 1 and 2, Customer requests 3 and 4.*

Review
Depending on timescales, allow children to share their work with each other, and then have one or more present to the class. Is the work clearly presented and easy to understand? Are children's calculations accurate? What would Gloria think? Would she be happy with their suggestions? If appropriate, would the customers be happy?

Further ideas
Visit local gardens (and if possible meet the gardeners.) Talk about the work involved in designing and maintaining a garden, and use the knowledge gained to redesign the children's own gardens.

Hi, I'm Gloria. I design gardens for people, at a price they can afford! I'm so busy that I need help, to keep all my customers happy and smiling.

Rules for designing and planning:

- Your garden must have:
  - Two flowerbeds
  - At least one bench
  - One shed
  - A fence

- Your garden can also have:
  - Trees
  - Gates
  - Play equipment
  - Bird baths
  - Statues

Presenting your work

- Draw a plan of your garden.

- Show all your calculations.

- How much does all the equipment and materials in your whole garden cost?

Take a look at this garden design.

This garden contains:

- 8 boxes of roses
- Path: woodchip
- Fence: wire mesh
- Shed: small tool shed
- Gate: plastic

Here is how I calculated the cost for everything.

Total cost:

8 boxes of roses = 8 x £5	=	£40
Path: woodchip	=	£30
Fence: wire mesh	=	£250
Shed: small tool shed	=	£65
Gate: plastic	=	£50
Total	=	<u>£435</u>

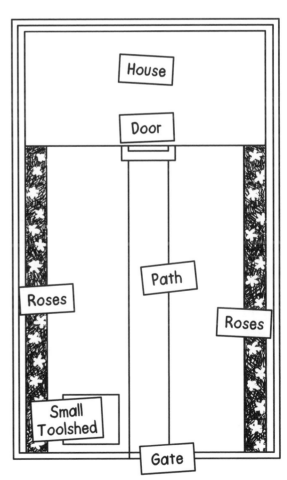

Flowers (cost for one box):

Pansies and crocus	Sunflowers	Tulips and daffodils	Roses of all colours
£2	£3	£4	£5

Paths (cost for one path):

Woodchip	Wooden boards	Pebbles	Paving stones
£30	£90	£90	£120

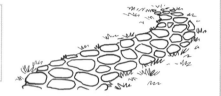

Fences:

Recycled chipboard	Pine panels	Wicker	Wire mesh
£100	£150	£200	£250

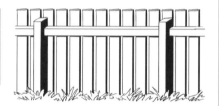

Trees (cost for one tree):

Apple	Rowan	Silver birch	Oak
£60	£80	£100	£120

Sheds:

Small tool shed	Large tool shed	Children's playhouse	Summer house
£65	£110	£150	£400

Extras:

Gates	Play equipment	Bird baths	Statues	Benches

Plastic: £50	Swing: £80	Basic: £10	Basic: £50	Basic: £60
Wood: £75	Slide: £100	Stylish: £20	Stylish: £80	Stylish: £100
Metal: £100	Climbing frame: £130	Deluxe: £30	Deluxe: £120	Deluxe: £150

Garden design sheet — Gloria's Glorious Gardens

■ Design your garden and work out how much it will cost.

Draw your garden here.

Use this space for your calculations.

Total cost: _____

Tips and ideas

While it might be too time-consuming for teachers to develop resources like those in this book, there are many opportunities to incorporate meaningful maths into engaging lessons. First and foremost, remember that 'word problems' are fine, but they are not the same as scenario-based activities where the maths is an integral part rather than an end in itself. As such, the following checklist and ideas have been provided as a starting point for developing your own activities:

Consider the context – make sure the activities use maths in a meaningful way.

Consider cross-curricular links – think about how maths is involved in each area of the curriculum.

Money Money Money – given that most maths we do in adult life centres around money, there should be no problem developing new ideas around cash.

Differentiation – this is the trickiest part of developing your own resources. Do you want to really challenge children, or consolidate their existing skills? (A mixture of both is recommended over time.)

Presenting work – how children present their work is very important for successful real-life maths work. Consider whether you want children to follow tight guidelines or allow them more freedom. The latter is particularly liberating for those used to laying out work in prescriptive ways.

Discussing work – we allow children to look at and discuss each other's literacy and topic work, so why not their maths? Talking about how they have presented their work, as well as the actual maths, can consolidate understanding.

Starting points

Your school:
- All about us. Collect information about everyone in the class and create charts to compare numbers, such as eye colour, favourite animals, and so on.
- How much of everything does your classroom have in it: pencils, paper, books?
- Do you have House systems or school sports days? Who organises the points system? Is it fair? Could there be a better system?
- Ask children with packed lunches to track their eating for a week. How many sandwiches does each child eat? How much food does the whole class eat? What about the school?
- Ask the children to help plan, prepare and run a healthy snack stall at break time.

Children's lives:
- Ask children to track which TV programmes they watch at home each week, and how long each programme lasts. How long do they spend watching TV each week?
- Walking to school. Estimate how far everyone walks to school, and how long it takes them. Use the figures to estimate how long it would take to walk longer distances.
- Find out when all your family's birthdays are. Create a calendar with key dates and reminders on.

Charity and enterprise:
- Support the children in running stalls and events to raise funds for charities.
- Run your own Scholastic Book Fair to raise funds: **www.bookfairs.scholastic.co.uk/business_school**